Walkthrough

What can you see in the picture? (*monkey*, *presents*)

Monkey has presents for all his animal friends.

Read the title, 'Animal Presents'.

Animal Presents

Will the monkey get a present?

Walkthrough

This is the blurb.

Let's read it together.

'Will the monkey get a present?' (Prompt suggestions.)

Animal Presents

Claire Llewellyn
Illustrated by Uwe Mayer

Walkthrough

This is the title page.

Let's read the title again, 'Animal Presents'.

We can see one of the presents here.

Here are the author's and illustrator's names.

This is the publisher's logo.

Walkthrough

Wow! What a big pile of presents monkey has.

Are they different shapes and sizes?

I wonder which present he will choose for each animal.

Observe and Prompt

Word Recognition

● Check the children can read the words 'This' 'is' and 'for'.
(These are sight words – words likely to be in their store of familiar words.)

Walkthrough

Who might this big, striped present be for?

Model quick page turning.

This is for . . .

3

Observe and Prompt

Language Comprehension

- Check the children make a quick page turn.
- Check the children understand what is happening at this point in the story.
- Ask the children who they think is the main character in the story.

Walkthrough

The tiger!
How did the monkey know that was the
tiger's present? (*stripes*)

the tiger.

4

 Observe and Prompt

Word Recognition

- Check the children can read the word 'the'. (This is also a sight word.)

- If the children have difficulty with the word 'tiger', ask them if they recognise the initial letter and sound – 't'. Then tell them this word and model the reading of it for them.

Walkthrough

What does this present look like?

Who do you think this is for?
(Model quick page turning again).

This is for . . .

5

 Observe and Prompt

Language Comprehension

- Check the children make a quick page turn and read with appropriate expression.
- Ask the children who the monkey gave its present to.
- Who do the children think the monkey might give this present to?

Walkthrough

The giraffe!

How did you know?

the giraffe.

6

👁 Observe and Prompt

Word Recognition

- The word 'giraffe' will not be decodable for the children at this stage. Tell them this word and model the reading of it for them.

Walkthrough

What sort of present is this?

It's enormous. Who is it for?

This is for . . .

7

Observe and Prompt

Language Comprehension

- Ask the children who the monkey gave the present to.
- How do the children think the giraffe feels? What might it say to the monkey?
- Who do the children think the next present might be for?

Walkthrough

Of course, the elephant.

the elephant.

8

 Observe and Prompt

Word Recognition

- The word 'elephant' may not be fully decodable for the children at this stage. Tell them this word and model the reading of it for them.
- Check the children are reading the sight words, 'This', 'is' and 'for' with confidence.

Walkthrough

Who is this present for?

Are there any clues which help you guess?

This is for . . .

9

 Observe and Prompt

Language Comprehension

- Check the children understand what is happening at this point in the story.
- Who else do the children think the monkey might give a present to?
- Ask the children who the next present might be for?

Walkthrough

The lion!

How did you guess?

the lion.

10

👁 Observe and Prompt

Word Recognition

- If the children have difficulty with the word 'lion', ask them if they recognise the initial letter and sound – 'l'. Then tell them the word and model the reading of it for them.

Walkthrough

What shape is this present?

Who is this present for?

This is for . . .

11

 **Observe and Prompt**

Language Comprehension

- Check the children have grasped the purpose of the ellipsis and are making quick page turns.

- Who do the children think the next present will be for? (*snake*)

- How can they tell? (*the shape*)

Walkthrough

Were you right?

What do you notice about the shape of the snake's present?

the snake.

👁 Observe and Prompt

Word Recognition

● The word 'snake' may not be decodable for the children at this stage. If they have difficulty with this word, ask them if they recognise the adjacent consonants – 'sn'. Then tell them the word and model the reading of it for them.

Walkthrough

Who could this present be for?

Why do you think that?

This is for . . .

13

Observe and Prompt

Language Comprehension

- Check the children are reading with appropriate expression.
- Ask the children why this present was for the snake? (*the shape*)
- What do the children think the snake might say to the monkey?

Yes, the zebra with its black and white stripes.

the zebra.

14

 Observe and Prompt

Word Recognition

- Check children are reading 'zebra' using their decoding skills. Can they blend the sounds all through the word?

Walkthrough

Who is the present for?

This is for . . .

15

Language Comprehension

- Check the children are reading with appropriate expression.
- How do the children think the zebra is feeling?
- Who do the children think the next present will be for?

Walkthrough

The monkey!

How does the monkey like his present? *(jumps up and down like a yo-yo)*

Was it easy to guess which present was for each animal?

the monkey!

16

 Observe and Prompt

Word Recognition

- If the children have difficulty with the word 'monkey', ask them if they recognise the initial letter and sound – 'm'. Then tell them this word and model the reading of it for them.

Language Comprehension

- Check the children understand what has happened at the end of the story. Who was the last present for?
- Ask the children to identify the characters in the picture.
- Do the children like to receive presents? What have been their favourite presents?